D0350653

Mind-Boggling Brain Teaser Puzzles
for Clued-up Kids

Managing Editor: Sarah Wells
Editor: Lucy Dear
Contributors: Fran Pickering, Philip Carter, Nick Daws,
Peter Sorrenti, Ann Marangos, Claire Redhead
Cover, page design and layout: Alan Shiner

Published by:
**Lagoon Books,
PO BOX 311, KT2 5QW, U.K.**

ISBN 1902813707

© 2003 Lagoon Books, London

Lagoon Books is a trade mark of
Lagoon Trading Company Limited.
All rights reserved.

Printed in Singapore

Other titles in the Mind-Boggling range include:

**MIND-BOGGLING
LATERAL THINKING PUZZLES
(For Clued-up Kids)**

**MIND-BOGGLING
TRICKY LOGIC PUZZLES
(For Clued-up Kids)**

**MIND-BOGGLING
CODE BREAKER PUZZLES
(For Clued-up Kids)**

MIND-BOGGLING
BRAIN TEASER PUZZLES
FOR CLUED-UP KIDS

Bored with everyday problems?
School slowly turning your brains into mush?
Then get your thinking gear into shape again with these
wickedly weird brain-teasers.

No special skills or knowledge are needed to solve
the puzzles in this book – just an agile mind and the
ability to see beyond the obvious.

Each puzzle has a rating from 1 (will give your brain a
light work-out) to 5 (seriously strenuous mental exercise).
The higher the difficulty level, the longer you can expect
to spend solving it.

The answers are at the back, but don't look up the
solution to a problem until you've had a good crack at it.
If you do, be prepared to kick yourself.
Often the answers are obvious once you see them.

So are you ready to put your brain through its paces
and bring it up to full power again? Great!
Then take a deep breath, turn the page,
and start puzzling!

Egg Scrambler

Difficulty Rating ☆

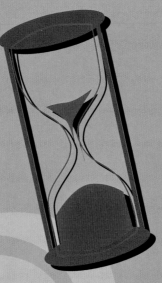

If it takes 85 seconds to boil two eggs,
how long will it take to boil three eggs?

City Conundrum

Difficulty Rating ☆☆

When does Chicago begin with a C
and end with an E?

Family Matters

Difficulty Rating ☆

My neighbor has four daughters,
and each daughter has a brother.
How many children does my neighbor have?

Breakfast Brain Ache

Difficulty Rating ☆☆☆☆☆

Every morning I eat two fried eggs for breakfast.
However, I do not buy them, steal them, borrow them,
exchange them, nor am I given them, and I do not
keep hens. How do I get them?

Eggsactly

Difficulty Rating ⭐⭐

Which is correct?
The yolks of the egg are white.
Or
The yolk of the eggs are white.

Clock Watching

Difficulty Rating ☆☆☆☆☆

Something must be wrong with my little digital clock. This morning I knew the correct time was well before 11 o'clock, yet the time on the dial was as shown below:

I then looked at it again nearly two hours later and the time display was again incorrect, or so I thought.

Some time later I felt rather silly, but at the same time relieved that there was nothing wrong with my alarm clock.

What was the explanation?

Five Hands

Difficulty Rating ☆☆☆

Many people walk about with five hands but no one
ever gives them a second glance. Why?

Bee Baffler

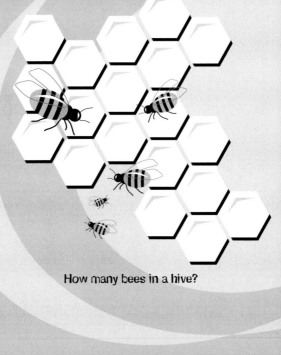

How many bees in a hive?

Candle Crazy

Difficulty Rating ☆☆

Which would burn longer,
a short fat red candle, a green square candle
or a long, thin pink candle?

Word Game

What is it that when you take away the whole,
you still have some left?

Mousy Mousy

Difficulty Rating ☆☆☆☆☆

A mouse hides 5 ears of corn in a tree trunk.
Every day he arrives at the tree trunk with two ears
and leaves with three. How long will it be before the
mouse removes all the ears from the tree trunk?

Basketball Betting

Difficulty Rating ✩✩

Tony bets Alan $10 that the score of the basketball game would be 0 – 0 before the game starts. Alan agrees, but loses the bet.
Why was it a certainty that Tony would win the bet?

Calendar Calamity

Difficulty Rating ☆☆☆

Sunday	Monday	Tuesday	Wednesday	Thursday	Friday	Saturday
1	2	3	4	5	6	7
8	9	10	11	12	13	14
15	16	17	18	19	20	21
22	23	24	25	26	27	28
29	30					

Where does Thursday always come
before Wednesday, and Friday always come
before Thursday?

Tied Up

Difficulty Rating ⭐⭐

A dog was tied to a lead which was 4 feet long.
Eight feet away was a juicy piece of meat.
How did the dog get to the meat?

Where in the World?

Difficulty Rating ☆☆

Where is it possible to find forests without trees,
roads without cars, towns without buildings
and rivers without water?

Letter Logic

Difficulty Rating ☆

M
T
W
T
F
S
?

What letter completes this sequence?

Apple Arithmetic

Difficulty Rating ★★☆

How many times is it possible to take away
9 apples from 54 apples?

Train Journey

Difficulty Rating ☆

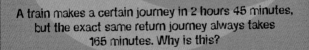

A train makes a certain journey in 2 hours 45 minutes, but the exact same return journey always takes 165 minutes. Why is this?

Water Retainer

Difficulty Rating ⭐⭐

What is full of holes, yet can hold water?

Wood Pile

Difficulty Rating ☆☆☆☆☆

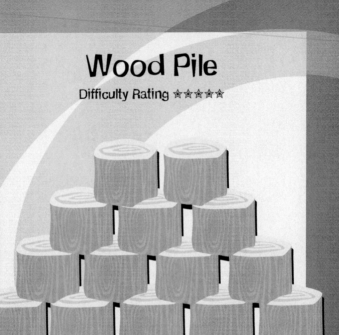

You cut up a piece of wood into 14 equal pieces
as firewood for yourself and your neighbor, and stack
them in two piles, each pile consisting of 7 pieces.
You then find you have three piles of wood.
Where has the other pile come from?

Girls Girls Girls

Difficulty Rating ☆

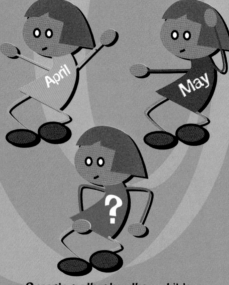

Susan's mother has three children.
The first is named April, the second is named May.
What is the name of the third child?

Up Up and Away

Difficulty Rating ☆☆☆

Imagine you are the pilot of Concorde.
The plane has flown from U.S.A. to Europe over
100 times. It was built in 1997 and is the pilot's first
command. What color eyes has the pilot?

Drawing Dilemma

Difficulty Rating ☆☆☆☆☆

What is wrong with this pair of scissors?

Hanky Puzzle

Difficulty Rating ☆☆☆☆

Jane throws out a challenge to Mary in the classroom.
"I'll put this ordinary pocket handkerchief on the floor.
You stand on one corner and I'll stand on the other
corner. Without either of us tearing, cutting, stretching
or altering it in any way, you won't be able to touch me."
How can this be done?

Figure It Out

Difficulty Rating ☆

Can you draw the next figure in this series?

Teasing Total

Difficulty Rating ★★★

Divide 100 by ½ and add 5.

Can you work out the answer to the sum above?

How Many Feet

Difficulty Rating ☆☆

A man walking his three dogs meets his brother
who is walking his two dogs.
How many feet are there in total when they meet?

Half and Half

Difficulty Rating ☆☆☆☆

From what whole number is it possible to take away half and leave nothing?

Family Fun

Difficulty Rating ☆☆☆

What relation is a child to its father
if it is not its father's own son?

Bedtime Drink

Difficulty Rating ☆☆

I decided to take a drink up to bed with me and,
although carrying it very carefully, tripped over one of
my toys on the bottom step and dropped the glass,
which shattered into a hundred pieces.
Despite this I did not spill a drop of milk. Why was that?

Easy Elephant

Difficulty Rating ☆

What do female elephants have that no other animals have?

Goodnight

Difficulty Rating ☆☆☆

What is the last thing you take off each
night before you get into bed?

Fill Up

Difficulty Rating ☆☆☆

By moving just one of the glasses,
can you arrange them so that empty and full
glasses alternate?
(Empty glass, full glass, empty glass, full glass etc).

Birthday Bonanza

Difficulty Rating ☆☆☆☆☆

Today is my birthday. The day before yesterday
I was 11 years old, but next year I will be 13 years old.
What date is my birthday?

Sum Stumper

Difficulty Rating ☆☆

If eight thousand eight hundred and eight dollars is written $8808, and nine thousand nine hundred and nine dollars is written $9909, how would you write twelve thousand, twelve hundred and 12 dollars?

Library Laughs

Difficulty Rating ☆☆☆

Sammy was a real bookworm who spent all his time in the local library. In just one month he worked his way through three volumes of an encyclopedia and two volumes of a dictionary, yet he could not remember one word that they contained. Why was that?

Book Baffler

Difficulty Rating ☆☆☆☆

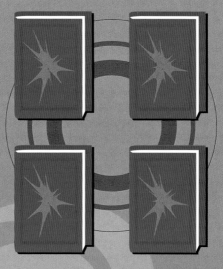

Change the position of one book only to produce
two straight lines with three books in each row.

Football Fan

Difficulty Rating ★★★

In the recent Football World Cup, who played for two different teams on the same evening?

Walkies

Difficulty Rating ✫✫✫✫

I took my dog for a walk. It did not walk in front of me,
nor did it walk behind me, nor did it walk to one side
of me. Where did it walk?

Adding Up

Difficulty Rating ☆☆☆

What can you add to one that will leave nothing?

Camping

Difficulty Rating ☆☆☆☆

The backpacker made his camp for the night but then
found he had only one match left. He wanted to light
his lantern, his camping stove and his pipe.
What should he light first?

Wedding Bells

Difficulty Rating ✸✸✸

Is it possible for a man to marry his widow's cousin?

Mix Up

Difficulty Rating ☆☆☆☆☆

How can you rearrange all the letters of the phrase
WRONG NOODLE into one long word?

It All Adds Up

Difficulty Rating ☆☆☆☆

$$1 + 1 + 1 = 142$$

Add just one line to make this calculation correct.

Puzzling Proverb

Difficulty Rating ☆☆☆

According to the proverb, two is company and three is a crowd.
What are four and five?

Spring Time

Difficulty Rating ☆☆☆☆☆

It is the beautiful month of May and in an English country garden there is an apple tree with seven branches, and on each branch are 40 leaves. The tree grows 5 new leaves on every branch each month. How many leaves will the tree have in 9 months time?

Gallop

Difficulty Rating ★★

A man went out riding at 10 p.m. on Tuesday
and returned at 6 a.m. the following day,
also on Tuesday. How is this possible?

Quick Sum

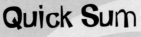

968249

Can you work out very quickly in your head the number that is double one half of 968249?

Pet Palaver

Difficulty Rating ☆☆

How many pets do I have if all but three are dogs,
all but three are guinea pigs, all but three are hamsters
and all but three are cats?

Day In History

Difficulty Rating ★★★★

My friend Matthew found an old coin the other day
and was so excited because it was marked 55 B.C.
However, I quickly convinced him that it must be a
forgery. How did I know this?

Leap Year

Difficulty Rating ☆☆

How many months have 29 days in a leap year?

Circular Sum

Difficulty Rating ☆☆☆

How many circles appear above?

Wet and Dry

Difficulty Rating☆☆

What do you keep in your house that gets wetter the more it dries?

Fishing Trip

Difficulty Rating ⭐⭐

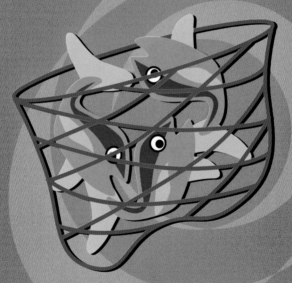

Two fathers and two sons went on a fishing trip.
Each caught one fish and returned home with it.
Why did they only have three fish between them?

To Sum Up

Difficulty Rating ☆☆☆☆☆

How is it possible to take two away from five
and leave just 4?

Belongings

Difficulty Rating ☆☆

What is it that was given to you, still belongs to you,
will always belong to you,
but is used by everyone you know?

Baby Celebrations

Difficulty Rating ★★★

A woman has two sons which were born
30 minutes apart. They are identical but not twins.
What is the explanation?

Road Trip

Difficulty Rating ☆

A man drove all the way from Chicago to Las Vegas only to then discover that he had had a flat tire for the entire journey. However, his car was completely unaffected by this and his journey was a smooth one. How is this possible?

Backwards
and Forwards

Difficulty Rating ☆☆

At the end of what sporting contest do the losers move forward and the winners move backward?

Million Dollars

Difficulty Rating ☆☆☆☆

A top brain-surgeon had a brother who won a million dollars on a lottery. However, the man who won the lottery did not have a brother. How could this be?

Animal Madness

Difficulty Rating ☆☆

How many pairs of animals did Moses take on the ark?

Word Up

Difficulty Rating ★★★★

Which 5-letter word is pronounced exactly the same
when its last four letters are removed from it?

Jumping Beans

Difficulty Rating ☆☆

Do you have any friends who are able to jump
higher than a house?

Southerly Winds

Difficulty Rating ☆☆

Somewhere on earth a flag sometimes flies which always
points to the south whichever way the wind blows.
How can this be possible?

Word Worrier

Difficulty Rating ✯✯✯

Can you think of a long word, which usually contains just one letter?

Start and Middle

Difficulty Rating ☆

PARIS EIFFEL TOWER RACE

?

What is in the middle of Paris, at the end of the Eiffel Tower, and is involved in starting every race?

Survivor

A plane crashes in the middle of the Atlantic Ocean exactly the same distance between U.S.A. and the British Isles. Where would the survivors be buried?

Missing Loot

Difficulty Rating ☆☆☆

Your friend tells you she has hidden a $10 bill between pages 31 and 32 in one of the books on the top shelf of the school library, and if you can find it you can keep it. However, you decide not to even go and look for it. Why is that?

All the Sixes

Difficulty Rating ☆☆☆☆

Can you think of a five-letter word that has six left when you take away two letters?

Extraordinary

Difficulty Rating ☆☆☆

If a peacock lays an egg in your garden,
would the egg be yours to keep?

Cash In

Difficulty Rating ☆

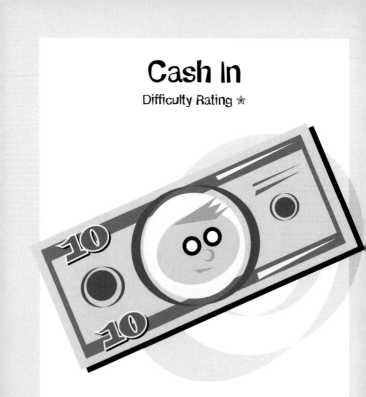

If there are twelve 10-dollar bills in a dozen,
how many 5-dollar bills are there in a dozen?

Odds On

Difficulty Rating ☆☆☆☆

11 - 2 = ?

How is it possible to take two away from eleven and
leave something that is not odd?

Coin Collection

Difficulty Rating ☆☆☆☆

Why are 2002 50-cent coins worth more than
2001 50-cent coins?

Sea Wall

Difficulty Rating ⭐⭐

If there were 11 gulls on a sea wall and a small boy shot one with a catapult, how many would be left?

Mountain High

Difficulty Rating ☆

What was the world's highest mountain before the discovery of Mount Everest?

Flower Power

Difficulty Rating ★★★

What kind of flower enables you to see it?

Head Count

Difficulty Rating ☆☆☆☆

Try adding these numbers up in your head.
Start by covering the bottom five numbers with your
hand and adding up just the first two numbers.
Then uncover them one at a time with your hand,
adding one number at a time to the total until you
have added all seven numbers.

Coin Set Up

Difficulty Rating ✫✫✫✫✫

Position these three coins so that two heads
are to the right of the line and two tails are
to the left of it.

Dictionary Challenge

Difficulty Rating ☆☆

How is it possible to spell a large word with just three letters?

Losing Out

Difficulty Rating ☆☆☆☆

Karen

Mark

Paul

Lucy Locket

What is it that Karen had first, Mark had last, Paul never had and Lucy Locket lost when she married Peter Piper?

Strawberry Pickers

Difficulty Rating ☆☆☆

If I pick strawberries at the rate of one every
5 seconds for one hour, how many can I put in
an empty box 5 inch wide and 3 inches deep in
90 minutes?

Butter Fingers

Difficulty Rating ☆☆

A man is looking for a coin that he has dropped on a carpeted floor. What is the first thing he does as soon as he finds it?

Solutions

Page 6 - Egg Scrambler
85 seconds, because you would put all three in the pan together.

Page 7 - City Conundrum
Always!
Chicago always begins with C and **E**nd always with E.

Page 8 - Family Matters
5.
Four daughters and one son. Each daughter has a brother, but it is, of course, the same person.

Page 9 - Breakfast Brain Ache
They are ducks' eggs – I keep ducks.

Page 10 - Eggsactly
Neither – the yolk of the egg is yellow.

Page 11 - Clock Watching
I had put the clock on the table upside down.
The time shown of 12:01 was, in fact, 10:21,
and the time of 11:21 was 12:11.

Page 12 - Five Hands
Because three of the hands are on their wrist watch. An hour hand, a minute hand and a second hand.

Page 13 - Bee Baffler
None.
It's spelt H-I-V-E.

Page 14 - Candle Crazy
None.
All candles burn shorter.

Page 15 - Word Game
The word **wholesome**!

Page 16 - Mousy Mousy
5 days.
Two of the ears are those on the side of his head.

Page 17 - Basketball Betting
The score is always 0 – 0 before the start of the game.

Page 18 - Calendar Calamity
In a dictionary.

Page 19 - Tied Up
Easily, as the other end of the lead was not tied to anything.

Page 20 - Where in the World?
On a map.

Page 21 - Letter Logic
S for Sunday.
The letters represent the initial letter of the days of the week.

Page 22 - Apple Arithmetic
Just once, after that you would be taking 9 apples away from 45 apples, then 9 from 36 apples, etc.

Page 23 - Train Journey
Because 2 hours 45 minutes is exactly the same as 165 minutes.

Page 24 - Water Retainer
A sponge.

Page 25 - Wood Pile
The third pile is sawdust from cutting up the wood.

Page 26 - Girls Girls Girls
Susan!

Page 27- Up Up and Away
Whatever is the color of your own eyes. Remember I said to imagine that you are the pilot.

Page 28 - Drawing Dilemma

If the handles are closed together then so should the blades. The blades only open on a pair of scissors when the handles are opened.

Page 29 - Hanky Puzzle

She puts the handkerchief under a door and stands on the corner at the other side of the door to Mary.

Page 30 - Figure It out

5.

They are the figures 1, 2, 3, 4, 5, when viewed in a mirror.

Page 31 - Teasing Total

205.

100 divided by 1/2 is 200 not 50, as every 1 has two halves, therefore, 100 has 200 halves.

Page 32 - How Many Feet

4 feet - belonging to the two men. Dogs have paws not feet.

Page 33 - Half And Half

8.

If you cut the figure 8 in half across its middle you're left with 2 zeros!

Page 34 - Family Fun

His daughter.

Page 35 - Bedtime Drink

The drink was orange juice, not milk.

Page 36 - Easy Elephant

Baby elephants.

Page 37 - Goodnight
Your feet off the floor.

Page 38 - Fill Up
Pick up the second glass and pour the water into the fifth glass, and then put the second glass back where it was.

Page 39 - Birthday Bonanza
December 31.
The statement was made on December 31, therefore, on December 30 I was 11. I am now 12 (on December 31) and next year on December 31 I will be 13.

Page 40 - Sum Stumper
$13212.

```
$12000+
$ 1200+
$   12
$13212
```

Page 41 - Library Laughs
Sammy was, indeed, a real bookworm, a little bug that eats its way through books.

Page 42 - Book Baffler
Pick up any one of the four books and put it on top of the book diagonally opposite.

Page 43 - Football Fan
The band, which played two national anthems for two different teams.

Page 44 - Walkies
It walked to the other side of me.

Page 45 - Adding Up
The letter N.
N + one = None.

Page 46 - Camping
The match!

Page 47 - Wedding Bells
No, because if he had a widow he would be dead!

Page 48 - Mix Up
WRONG NOODLE is an anagram of ONE LONG WORD.

Page 49 - It All Adds Up
Add an extra line to the first plus sign changing it to a 4.

$$1 + 1 + 1 = 142$$

Page 50 - Puzzling Proverb
Four and five are nine!
(4 + 5 = 9).

Page 51 - Spring Time
None!
In 9 months it will be January, and apple trees will have lost all their leaves in the Winter.

Page 52 - Gallop
His horse was called Tuesday.

Page 53 - Quick Sum
968249.
Double one half of anything is the same thing.

Page 54 - Pet Palaver
Four pets
A dog, a guinea pig, a hamster and a cat.

Page 55 - Day in History
B.C. stands for Before Christ. A person could not mark a coin B.C. before the birth of Christ, because he would not have known that Christ would exist in the future, so it must be a forgery.

Page 56 - Leap Year
They all do. Some have more, but all have at least 29. February has 29 days in a leap year.

Page 57 - Circular Sum
One circle, the one in the middle. The rest are not circles because they are incomplete.

Page 58 - Wet and Dry
A towel.

Page 59 - Fishing Trip
There were only three men, grandfather, father and son.

Page 60 - To Sum Up
Take the letters F and E away from FIVE to leave IV, which is 4 in Roman numerals.

Page 61 - Belongings
Your name.

Page 62 - Baby Celebrations
They are triplets and the third is a girl.

Page 63 - Road Trip
It was his spare tire that was flat.

Page 64 - Backwards and Forwards
Tug-of-War.

Page 65 - Million Dollars
The brain-surgeon was a woman!

Page 66 - Animal Madness
None, it was Noah who took the animals on the ark.

Page 67 - Word Up
Queue. Q.

Page 68 - Jumping Beans
Yes, all of them. A house cannot jump.

Page 69 - Southerly Winds
It stands exactly on the North Pole where everything points to the South whichever way you turn.

Page 70 - Word Worrier
Envelope.
'Envelope' is a long word and an envelope usually only contains one letter.

Page 71 - Start and Middle
The Letter R.

Page 72 - Survivor
Nowhere, as the survivors would still be alive.

Page 73 - Missing Loot
Because pages 31 and 32 are always the same sheet of paper, front and back, so there cannot be a $10 bill hidden between them.

Page 74 - All the Sixes
The word SIXTY. If you take away the last two letters you are left with SIX.

Page 75 - Extraordinary
No, because the egg would not exist. Peacocks do not lay eggs as they are male. Peahens lay eggs!

Page 76 - Cash In
12.
There are twelve of anything in a dozen!

Page 77 - Odds On
ELEVEN minus the letters EL leave EVEN.

Page 78 - Coin Collection
2002 50 cent coins = 2002 x $0.50 = $1001.00
2001 50 cent coins = 2001 x $0.50 = $1000.50.
Therefore 2002 50 cent coins are worth an extra 50c.

Page 79 - Sea Wall
Only the dead one. The others would fly away.

Page 80 - Mountain High
Mount Everest!
It was always there, even before
it had been discovered.

Page 81 - Flower Power
Iris.
(As well as being a flower name,
each of your eyes has an Iris).

Page 82 - Head Count
4100.
Many people get 5000 because
when they add the final 20 to the
total of the first six figures (4080)
in their head they jump to 5000
instead of 4100.

Page 83 - Coin Set Up

Page 84 - Dictionary Challenge
Big.

Page 85 - Losing Out
The letter K.

Page 86 - Strawberry Pickers
Only one - after that the box
would not be empty.

Page 87 - Butter Fingers
Stops looking for it!